HANGMAN

Fill in letters as they are guessed.

A B C D E F G H I J K L M
N O P Q R S T U V W X Y Z

HANGMAN

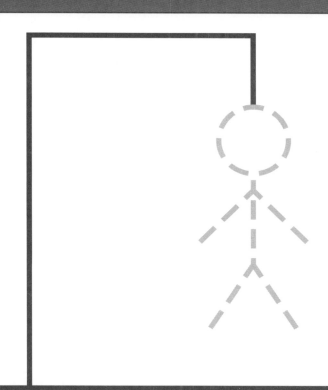

Fill in letters as they are guessed.

ABCDEFGHIJKLM
NOPQRSTUVWXYZ

HANGMAN

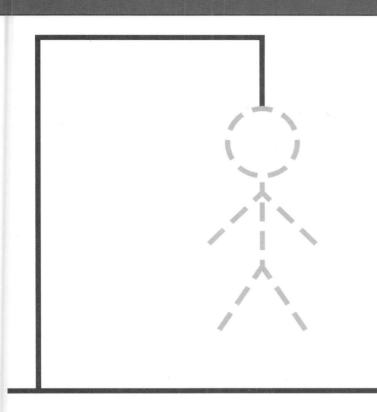

Fill in letters as they are guessed.

ABCDEFGHIJKLM
NOPQRSTUVWXYZ

HANGMAN

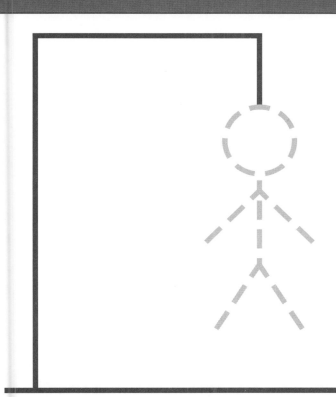

Fill in letters as they are guessed.

ABCDEFGHIJKLM
NOPQRSTUVWXYZ

HANGMAN

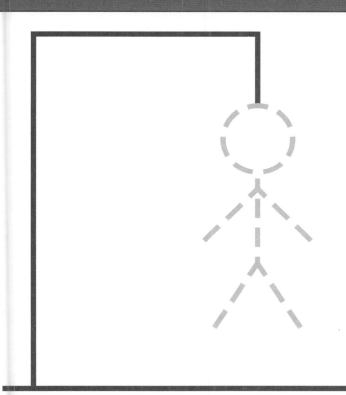

Fill in letters as they are guessed.

ABCDEFGHIJKLM
NOPQRSTUVWXYZ

HANGMAN

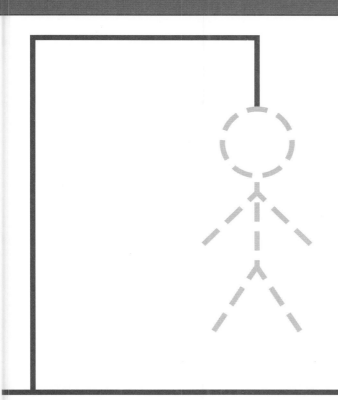

Fill in letters as they are guessed.

ABCDEFGHIJKLM
NOPQRSTUVWXYZ

HANGMAN

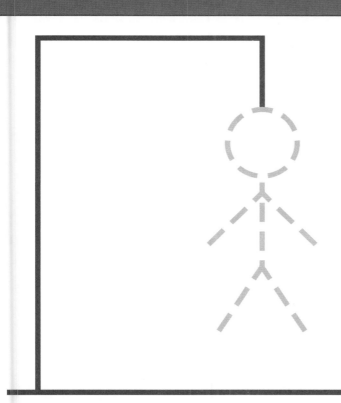

Fill in letters as they are guessed.

ABCDEFGHIJKLM
NOPQRSTUVWXYZ

HANGMAN

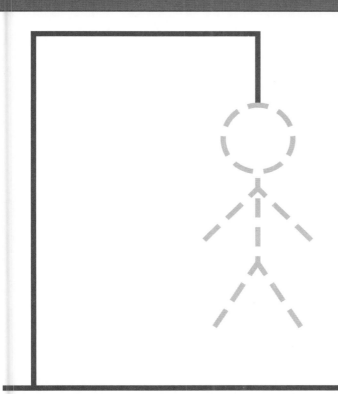

Fill in letters as they are guessed.

ABCDEFGHIJKLM
NOPQRSTUVWXYZ

HANGMAN

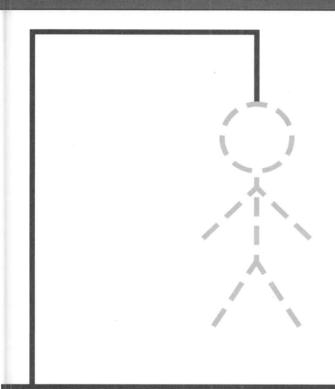

Fill in letters as they are guessed.

ABCDEFGHIJKLM
NOPQRSTUVWXYZ

HANGMAN

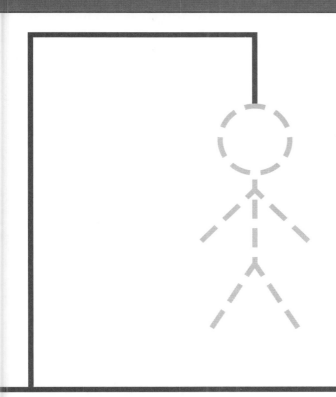

Fill in letters as they are guessed.

ABCDEFGHIJKLM
NOPQRSTUVWXYZ

HANGMAN

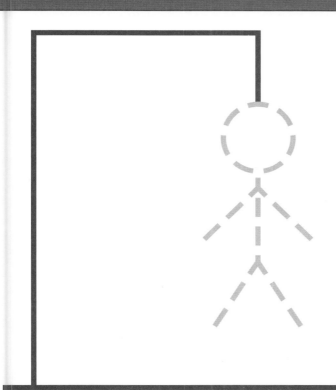

Fill in letters as they are guessed.

ABCDEFGHIJKLM
NOPQRSTUVWXYZ

HANGMAN

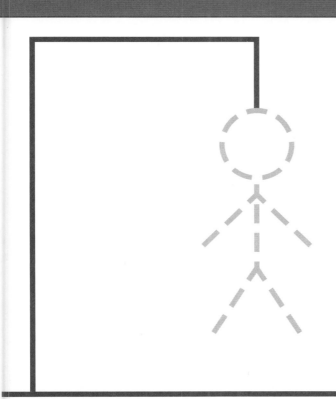

Fill in letters as they are guessed.

ABCDEFGHIJKLM
NOPQRSTUVWXYZ

FORTUNE TELLER

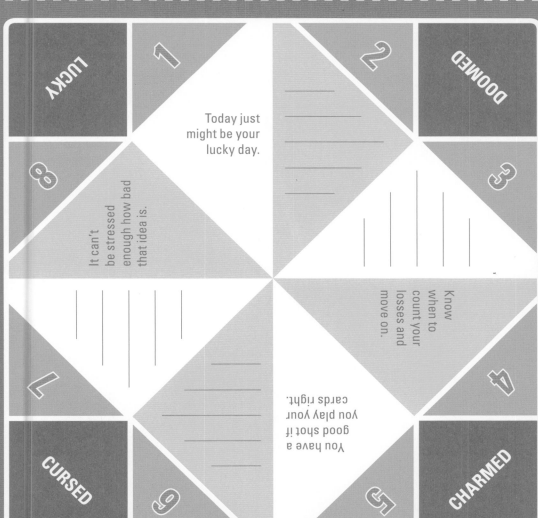

LUCKY

DOOMED

Today just might be your lucky day.

It can't be stressed enough how bad that idea is.

Know when to count your losses and move on.

You have a good shot if you play your cards right.

CURSED

CHARMED

FORTUNE TELLER

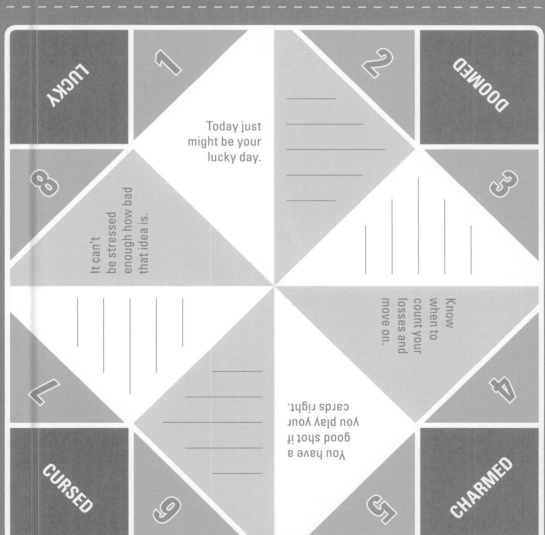

LUCKY

DOOMED

CURSED

CHARMED

Today just might be your lucky day.

It can't be stressed enough how bad that idea is.

Know when to count your losses and move on.

You have a good shot if you play your cards right.

FORTUNE TELLER

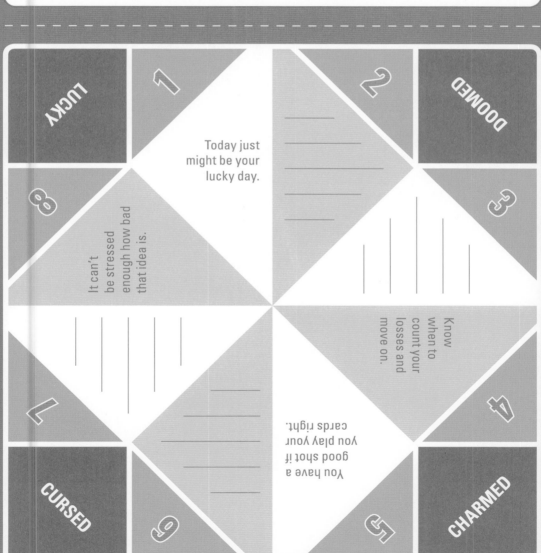

LUCKY   1   2   DOOMED

Today just might be your lucky day.

8

It can't be stressed enough how bad that idea is.

3

Know when to count your losses and move on.

7

You have a good shot if you play your cards right.

CURSED   6   5   CHARMED   4

FORTUNE TELLER

WHO:

DATE:

QUESTION:

FATE:

☐ WISE WORDS   ☐ NEITHER HERE NOR THERE   ☐ FOR THE BIRDS   ☐ TRY, TRY AGAIN

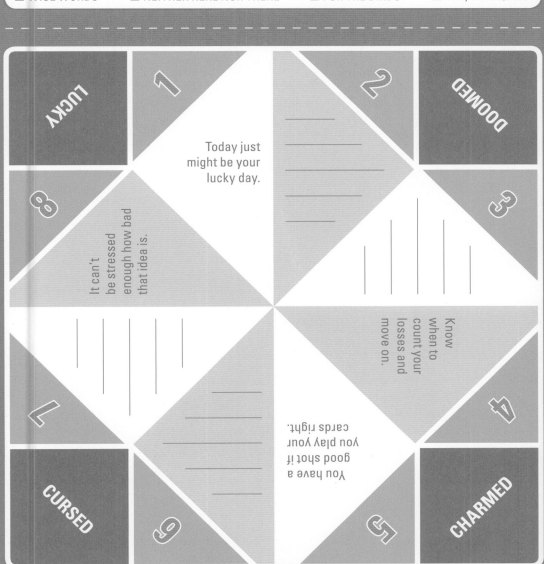

LUCKY

1

2

DOOMED

8

3

Today just might be your lucky day.

It can't be stressed enough how bad that idea is.

Know when to count your losses and move on.

7

4

CURSED

6

5

CHARMED

You have a good shot if you play your cards right.

FORTUNE TELLER

WHO: _____ **DATE:** _____

QUESTION: _____
_____

FATE: _____
_____

☐ WISE WORDS   ☐ NEITHER HERE NOR THERE   ☐ FOR THE BIRDS   ☐ TRY, TRY AGAIN

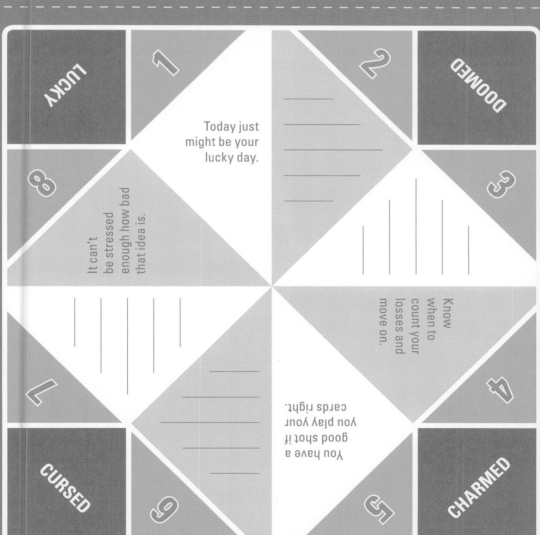

LUCKY

1

2

DOOMED

8

3

Today just might be your lucky day.

It can't be stressed enough how bad that idea is.

Know when to count your losses and move on.

7

4

You have a good shot if you play your cards right.

CURSED

6

5

CHARMED

FORTUNE TELLER

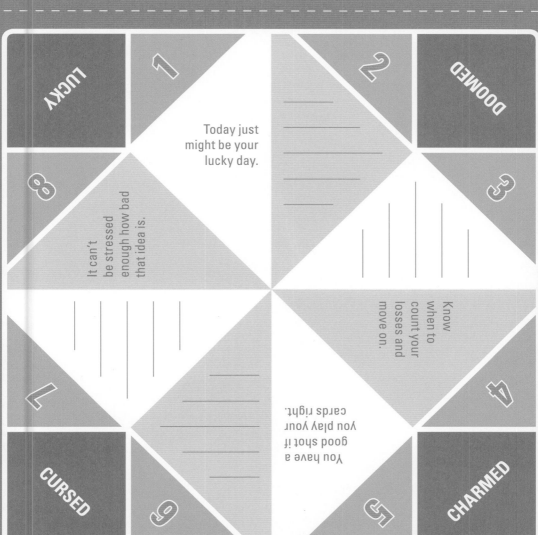

LUCKY

1

2

DOOMED

Today just might be your lucky day.

8

3

It can't be stressed enough how bad that idea is.

Know when to count your losses and move on.

7

4

You have a good shot if you play your cards right.

CURSED

6

5

CHARMED

FORTUNE TELLER

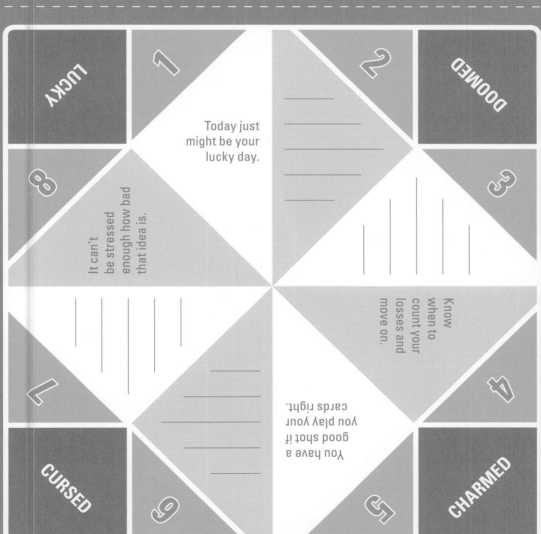

LUCKY

DOOMED

Today just might be your lucky day.

It can't be stressed enough how bad that idea is.

Know when to count your losses and move on.

You have a good shot if you play your cards right.

CURSED

CHARMED

FORTUNE TELLER

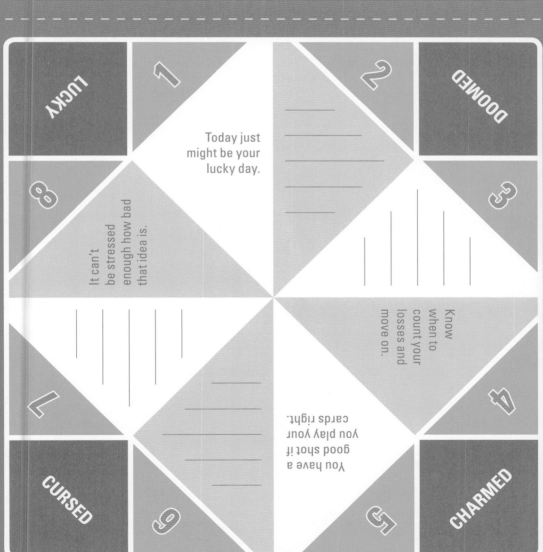

LUCKY

1

2

DOOMED

8

3

Today just might be your lucky day.

It can't be stressed enough how bad that idea is.

Know when to count your losses and move on.

7

4

You have a good shot if you play your cards right.

CURSED

6

5

CHARMED

FORTUNE TELLER

KNOCKKNOCKSTUFF.COM • © 2012 KNOCK KNOCK LLC

WHO: **DATE:**

QUESTION:

FATE:

☐ WISE WORDS   ☐ NEITHER HERE NOR THERE   ☐ FOR THE BIRDS   ☐ TRY, TRY AGAIN

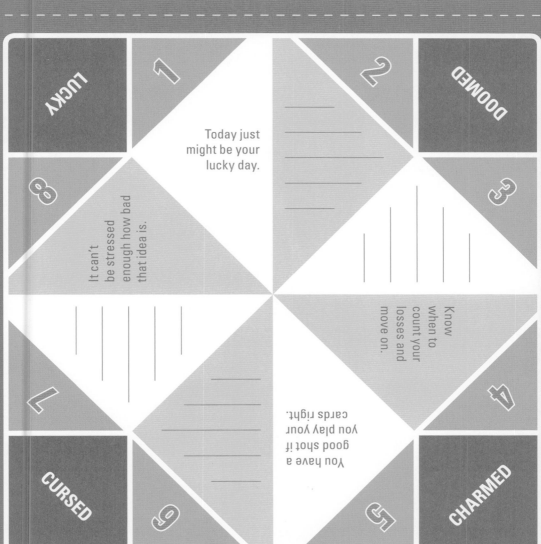

LUCKY   1   2   DOOMED

8   3

Today just might be your lucky day.

It can't be stressed enough how bad that idea is.

Know when to count your losses and move on.

You have a good shot if you play your cards right.

7   4

CURSED   6   5   CHARMED

FORTUNE TELLER

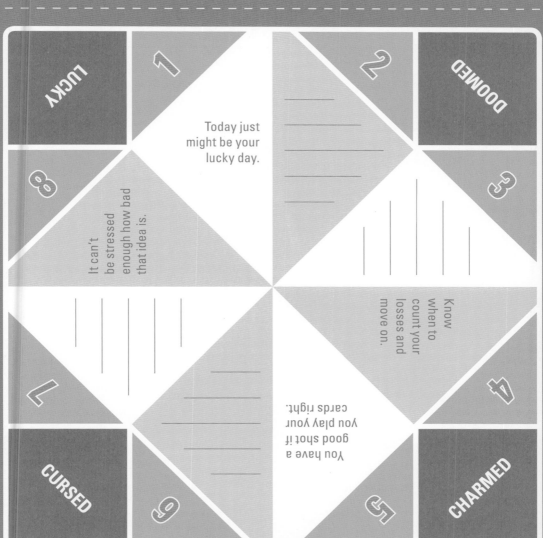

LUCKY

1

2

DOOMED

8

Today just might be your lucky day.

3

It can't be stressed enough how bad that idea is.

Know when to count your losses and move on.

7

You have a good shot if you play your cards right.

CURSED

6

5

CHARMED

FORTUNE TELLER

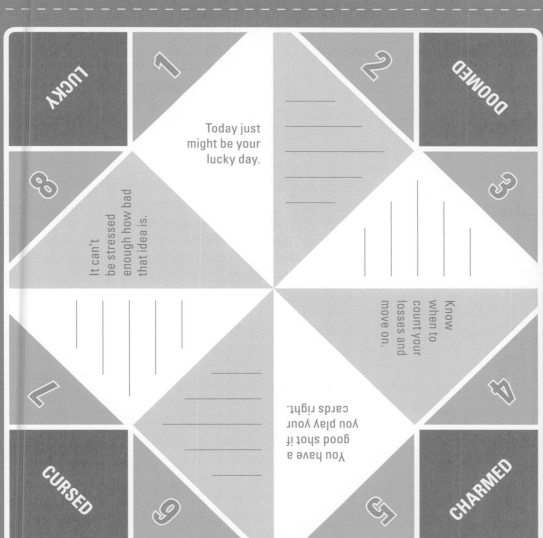

LUCKY   1   2   DOOMED

8   3

7   4

CURSED   6   5   CHARMED

Today just might be your lucky day.

It can't be stressed enough how bad that idea is.

Know when to count your losses and move on.

You have a good shot if you play your cards right.

FORTUNE TELLER

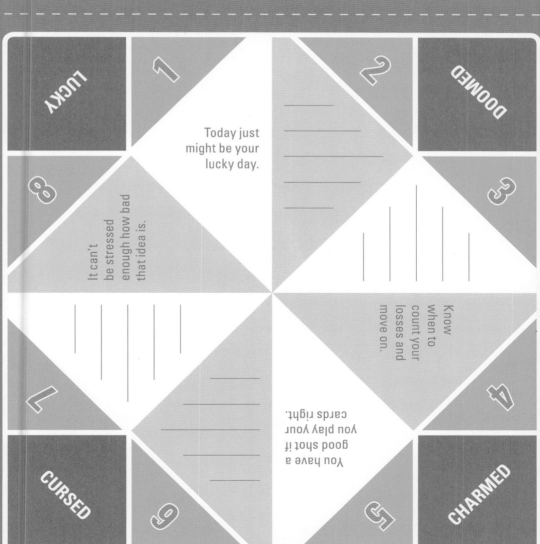

LUCKY

1

2

DOOMED

8

Today just might be your lucky day.

3

It can't be stressed enough how bad that idea is.

Know when to count your losses and move on.

7

You have a good shot if you play your cards right.

4

CURSED

6

5

CHARMED

TIC-TAC-TOE

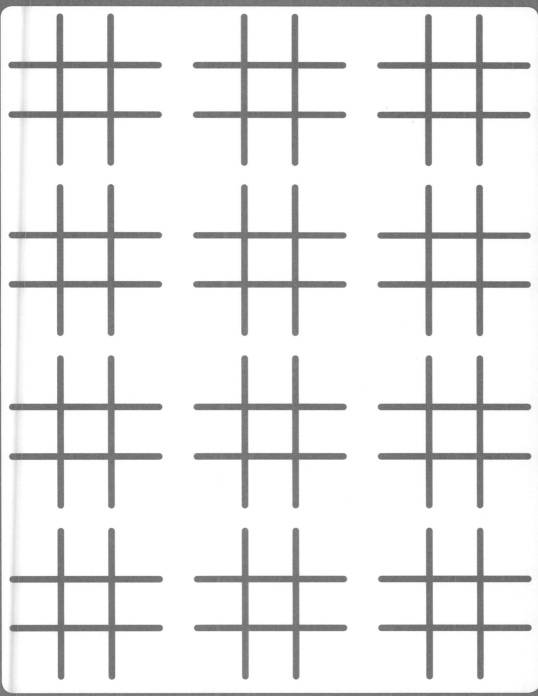

TIC-TAC-TOE

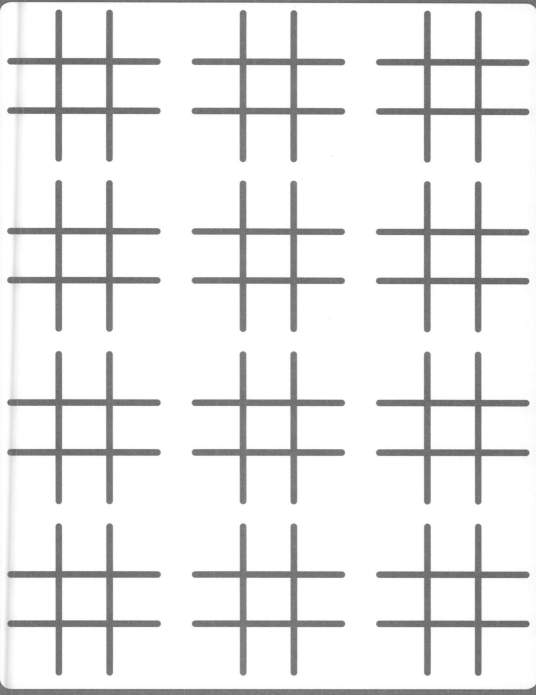

TIC-TAC-TOE

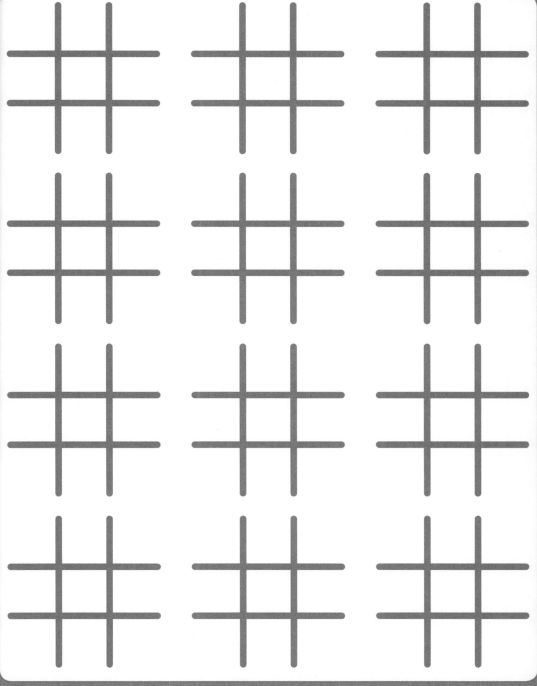

TIC-TAC-TOE

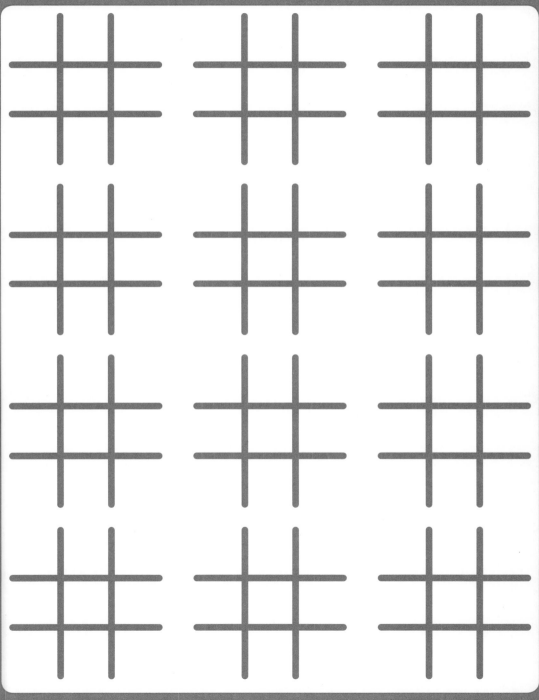

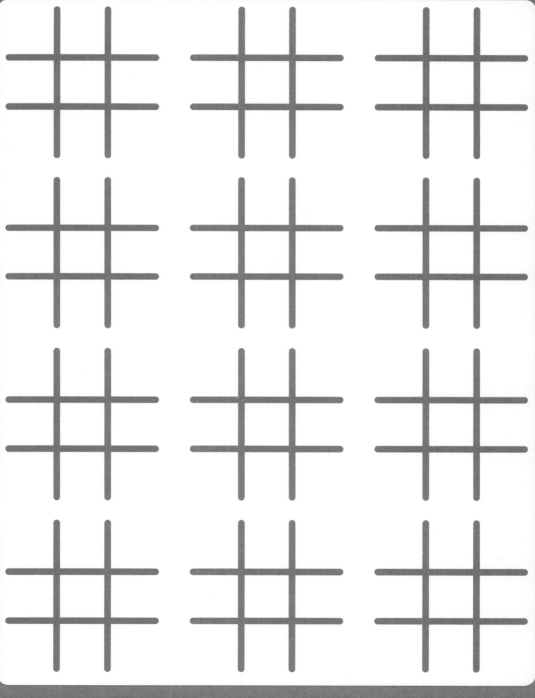

TIC-TAC-TOE

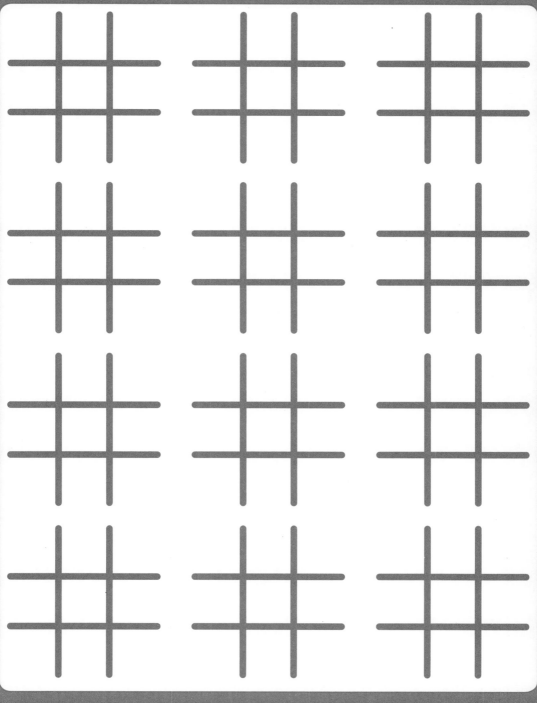

TIC-TAC-TOE

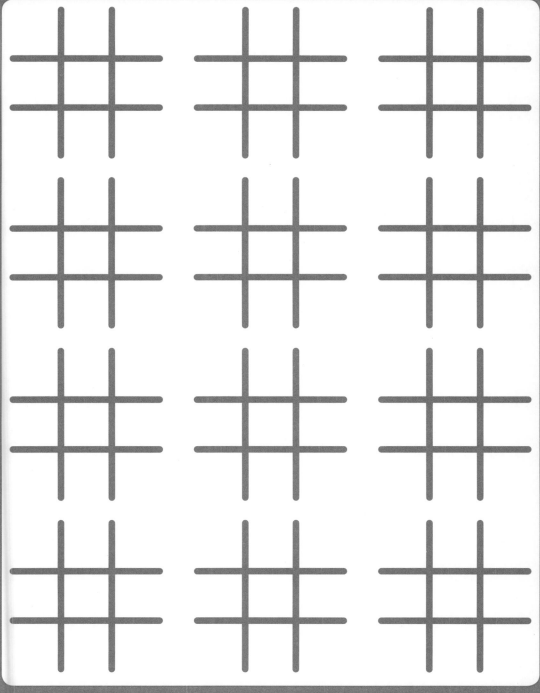

TIC-TAC-TOE

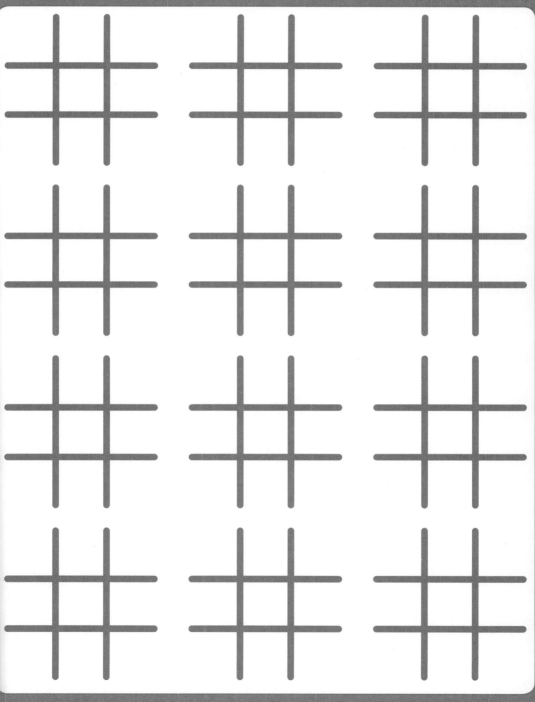

TIC-TAC-TOE

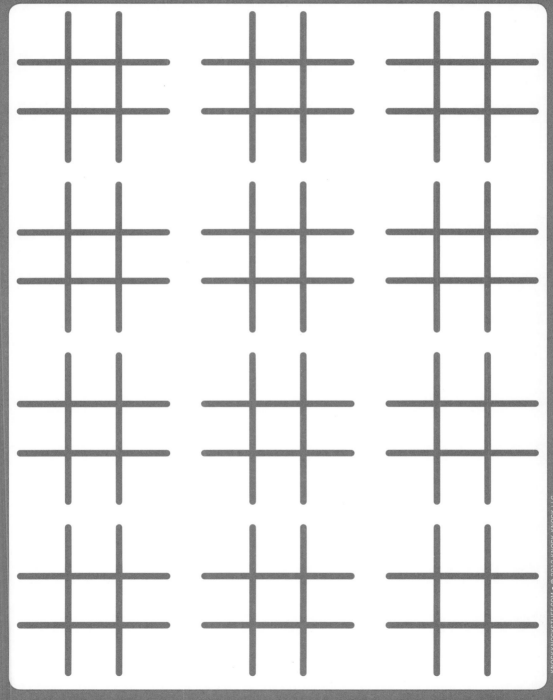

TIC-TAC-TOE

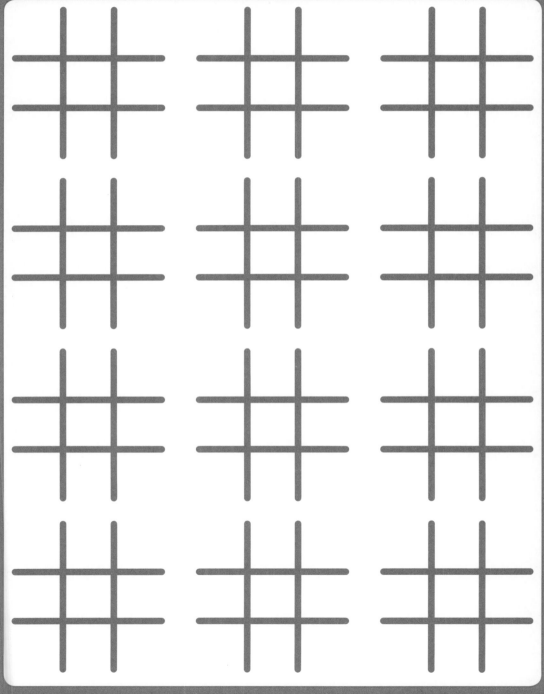

TIC-TAC-TOE

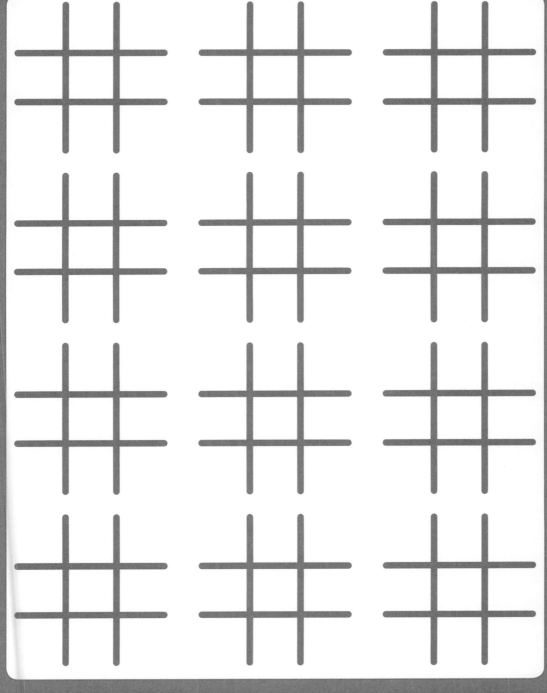

TIC-TAC-TOE

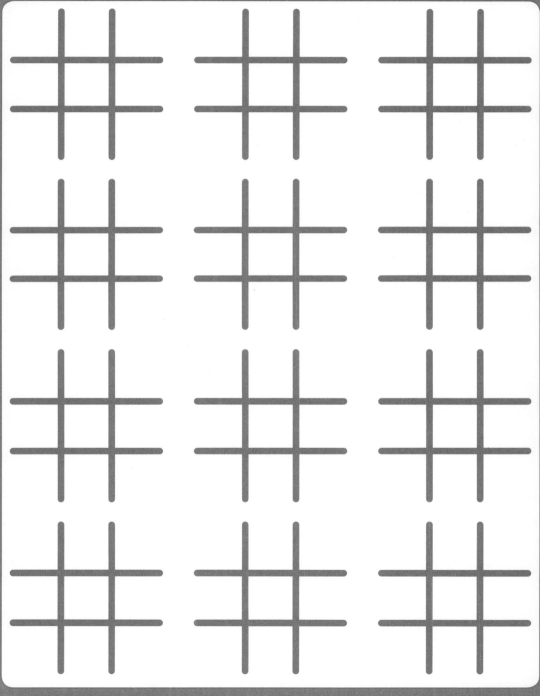

CATEGORIES

Circle the letter in play.

A B C D E F G H I J K L M N O P Q R S T U V W X Y Z

FICTIONAL CHARACTER	FRUIT	COUNTRY
TELEVISION SHOW	SILLY THING	FOUND IN AN OFFICE
SONG TITLE	ANIMAL	DESSERT

Circle the letter in play.

A B C D E F G H I J K L M N O P Q R S T U V W X Y Z

CARTOON CHARACTER	VEGETABLE	CITY
CELEBRITY	ANNOYING THING	FOUND IN A KITCHEN
MOVIE TITLE	OCCUPATION	GAME

CATEGORIES

Circle the letter in play.

A B C D E F G H I J K L M N O P Q R S T U V W X Y Z

FICTIONAL CHARACTER	FRUIT	COUNTRY
TELEVISION SHOW	SILLY THING	FOUND IN AN OFFICE
SONG TITLE	ANIMAL	DESSERT

Circle the letter in play.

A B C D E F G H I J K L M N O P Q R S T U V W X Y Z

CARTOON CHARACTER	VEGETABLE	CITY
CELEBRITY	ANNOYING THING	FOUND IN A KITCHEN
MOVIE TITLE	OCCUPATION	GAME

CATEGORIES

Circle the letter in play.

A B C D E F G H I J K L M N O P Q R S T U V W X Y Z

FICTIONAL CHARACTER	FRUIT	COUNTRY
TELEVISION SHOW	SILLY THING	FOUND IN AN OFFICE
SONG TITLE	ANIMAL	DESSERT

Circle the letter in play.

A B C D E F G H I J K L M N O P Q R S T U V W X Y Z

CARTOON CHARACTER	VEGETABLE	CITY
CELEBRITY	ANNOYING THING	FOUND IN A KITCHEN
MOVIE TITLE	OCCUPATION	GAME

CATEGORIES

Circle the letter in play.

A B C D E F G H I J K L M N O P Q R S T U V W X Y Z

FICTIONAL CHARACTER	FRUIT	COUNTRY
TELEVISION SHOW	SILLY THING	FOUND IN AN OFFICE
SONG TITLE	ANIMAL	DESSERT

Circle the letter in play.

A B C D E F G H I J K L M N O P Q R S T U V W X Y Z

CARTOON CHARACTER	VEGETABLE	CITY
CELEBRITY	ANNOYING THING	FOUND IN A KITCHEN
MOVIE TITLE	OCCUPATION	GAME

CATEGORIES

A B C D E F G H I J K L M N O P Q R S T U V W X Y Z

FICTIONAL CHARACTER	FRUIT	COUNTRY
TELEVISION SHOW	SILLY THING	FOUND IN AN OFFICE
SONG TITLE	ANIMAL	DESSERT

A B C D E F G H I J K L M N O P Q R S T U V W X Y Z

CARTOON CHARACTER	VEGETABLE	CITY
CELEBRITY	ANNOYING THING	FOUND IN A KITCHEN
MOVIE TITLE	OCCUPATION	GAME

CATEGORIES

Circle the letter in play.

A B C D E F G H I J K L M N O P Q R S T U V W X Y Z

FICTIONAL CHARACTER	FRUIT	COUNTRY
TELEVISION SHOW	SILLY THING	FOUND IN AN OFFICE
SONG TITLE	ANIMAL	DESSERT

Circle the letter in play.

A B C D E F G H I J K L M N O P Q R S T U V W X Y Z

CARTOON CHARACTER	VEGETABLE	CITY
CELEBRITY	ANNOYING THING	FOUND IN A KITCHEN
MOVIE TITLE	OCCUPATION	GAME

CATEGORIES

Circle the letter in play.

A B C D E F G H I J K L M N O P Q R S T U V W X Y Z

FICTIONAL CHARACTER	FRUIT	COUNTRY
TELEVISION SHOW	SILLY THING	FOUND IN AN OFFICE
SONG TITLE	ANIMAL	DESSERT

Circle the letter in play.

A B C D E F G H I J K L M N O P Q R S T U V W X Y Z

CARTOON CHARACTER	VEGETABLE	CITY
CELEBRITY	ANNOYING THING	FOUND IN A KITCHEN
MOVIE TITLE	OCCUPATION	GAME

CATEGORIES

Circle the letter in play.

A B C D E F G H I J K L M N O P Q R S T U V W X Y Z

FICTIONAL CHARACTER	FRUIT	COUNTRY
TELEVISION SHOW	SILLY THING	FOUND IN AN OFFICE
SONG TITLE	ANIMAL	DESSERT

Circle the letter in play.

A B C D E F G H I J K L M N O P Q R S T U V W X Y Z

CARTOON CHARACTER	VEGETABLE	CITY
CELEBRITY	ANNOYING THING	FOUND IN A KITCHEN
MOVIE TITLE	OCCUPATION	GAME

CATEGORIES

A B C D E F G H I J K L M N O P Q R S T U V W X Y Z

FICTIONAL CHARACTER	FRUIT	COUNTRY
TELEVISION SHOW	SILLY THING	FOUND IN AN OFFICE
SONG TITLE	ANIMAL	DESSERT

A B C D E F G H I J K L M N O P Q R S T U V W X Y Z

CARTOON CHARACTER	VEGETABLE	CITY
CELEBRITY	ANNOYING THING	FOUND IN A KITCHEN
MOVIE TITLE	OCCUPATION	GAME

CATEGORIES

A B C D E F G H I J K L M N O P Q R S T U V W X Y Z

FICTIONAL CHARACTER	FRUIT	COUNTRY
TELEVISION SHOW	SILLY THING	FOUND IN AN OFFICE
SONG TITLE	ANIMAL	DESSERT

A B C D E F G H I J K L M N O P Q R S T U V W X Y Z

CARTOON CHARACTER	VEGETABLE	CITY
CELEBRITY	ANNOYING THING	FOUND IN A KITCHEN
MOVIE TITLE	OCCUPATION	GAME

CATEGORIES

A B C D E F G H I J K L M N O P Q R S T U V W X Y Z

FICTIONAL CHARACTER	FRUIT	COUNTRY
TELEVISION SHOW	SILLY THING	FOUND IN AN OFFICE
SONG TITLE	ANIMAL	DESSERT

Circle the letter in play.

A B C D E F G H I J K L M N O P Q R S T U V W X Y Z

CARTOON CHARACTER	VEGETABLE	CITY
CELEBRITY	ANNOYING THING	FOUND IN A KITCHEN
MOVIE TITLE	OCCUPATION	GAME

CATEGORIES

Circle the letter in play.

A B C D E F G H I J K L M N O P Q R S T U V W X Y Z

FICTIONAL CHARACTER	FRUIT	COUNTRY
TELEVISION SHOW	SILLY THING	FOUND IN AN OFFICE
SONG TITLE	ANIMAL	DESSERT

Circle the letter in play.

A B C D E F G H I J K L M N O P Q R S T U V W X Y Z

CARTOON CHARACTER	VEGETABLE	CITY
CELEBRITY	ANNOYING THING	FOUND IN A KITCHEN
MOVIE TITLE	OCCUPATION	GAME

DOTS & BOXES

DOTS & BOXES

DOTS & BOXES

DOTS & BOXES

DOTS & BOXES

DOTS & BOXES

DOTS & BOXES

DOTS & BOXES

DOTS & BOXES

DOTS & BOXES

DOTS & BOXES

DOTS & BOXES